T

GRADE

1

The Syllabus of Examinations should be read for details of requirements, especially those for scales, aural tests and sight-reading. Attention should be paid to the Special Notices on the front inside cover, where warning is given of changes.

The syllabus is obtainable from music dealers or from The Associated Board of the Royal Schools of Music, 14 Bedford Square, London WC1B 3JG (please send a stamped addressed C5 envelope).

In centres outside the UK, information may be obtained from the Local Representative.

REQUIREMENTS

SCALES, ARPEGGIOS AND BROKEN CHORDS
(from memory)

Scales
(i) each hand separately, up and down
(*or* down and up in L.H. at candidate's choice)
in the following keys:
C, G, D, F majors and A, D minors
(melodic *or* harmonic minor at candidate's choice)
(all two octaves)
(ii) in contrary motion, both hands beginning and ending on the key-note (unison), in the key of C major only (one octave)

Arpeggios
the common chords of C, G and F majors, and A and D minors, in root position only, each hand separately (one octave)

Broken Chords
formed from the chords of C, G and F majors, and A and D minors, each hand separately, according to the pattern shown in the syllabus

PLAYING AT SIGHT (see current syllabus)

AURAL TESTS (see current syllabus)

THREE PIECES

LIST A		*page*
1	**Johann Christian Bach** (1735–1782) Aria in F, BWV Anh. II 131, from *The Anna Magdalena Bach Book of 1725*	2
2	**Muzio Clementi** (1752–1832) Arietta in C, Op. 42, Lesson 5	3
3	**Anon.** Menuet in F, No. 6 from L. Mozart's *Nannerl-Notenbuch*	4

LIST B		
1	**William Alwyn** (1905–1985) The Pear Tree is Laden with Fruit	5
2	**Félix Le Couppey** (1811–1887) Melody in C, No. 21 from *A. B. C. du Piano*	6
3	**Daniel Gottlob Türk** (1750–1813) Arioso in F, No. 1 from *Zwölf Handstücke*	7

LIST C		
1	**Richard Rodney Bennett** 'Friday', from *Seven Days a Week*	8
2	**Stephen Duro** 'Calypso Joe', No. 9 from *Finger Jogging Boogie*	9
3	**William Gillock** The Swinging Sioux	10

Candidates must prepare three pieces, one from each of the three Lists, A, B and C. Candidates may choose from the pieces printed in this volume or any other piece listed for the grade. Full lists are given in the syllabus and on the inside covers of the *Selected Piano Examination Pieces, 1999–2000*.

Editor for the Associated Board: **Richard Jones**

Where appropriate, pieces have been checked with original source material and edited as necessary for instructional purposes. Fingering, phrasing, pedalling, metronome marks and the editorial realization of ornaments (where given) are for guidance but are not comprehensive or obligatory.

2

A:1

Aria in F

BWV Anh. II 131, from *The Anna Magdalena Bach Book of 1725*

J. C. BACH

This piece is one of the earliest compositions by Bach's youngest son Johann Christian, written when he was still a child. Unmarked crotchets should be lightly detached. The *staccato* wedges and slur in the R.H. of bars 12–14 are the composer's own; all other marks of phrasing and articulation and the dynamics are editorial suggestions only.
Source: Staatsbibliothek zu Berlin, Preussischer Kulturbesitz, Mus. ms. Bach P225.

Selected from J. S. Bach *et al.*, *The Anna Magdalena Bach Book of 1725*, edited by Richard Jones (Associated Board)

Melody in C

No. 21 from *A. B. C. du Piano*

LE COUPPEY

This piece is taken from a piano textbook by Félix Le Couppey (1811–87), a pupil, and later teacher, at the Paris Conservatoire. The L.H. quavers should be played *sempre legato*. The slurs in the R.H. of bars 1 & 3 are editorial suggestions only.
Source: *A. B. C. du piano, méthode pour les commençants* (Leipzig, 1859).

The Pear Tree is Laden with Fruit

ALWYN

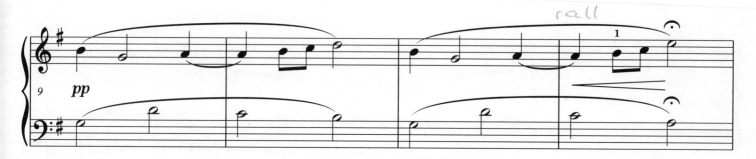

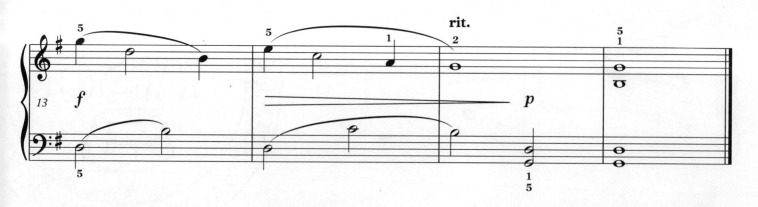

William Alwyn (1905–85) was an English composer who taught at the Royal Academy of Music for 30 years and is well known for his large output of film music.

A:3

Menuet in F

No. 6 from L. Mozart's *Nannerl-Notenbuch*

ANON.

This piece is taken from a collection that Leopold Mozart compiled in 1759 for his eight-year-old daughter Marie Anne, nicknamed Nannerl (sister of Wolfgang Amadeus), whom he was at that time teaching to play the piano. Crotchets should be lightly detached throughout. Slurs and dynamics are editorial suggestions only.

Source: L. Mozart's *Nannerl-Notenbuch* of 1759, original manuscript, property of the Internationale Stiftung Mozarteum, Salzburg.

3

Arietta in C
Op. 42, Lesson 5

CLEMENTI

Muzio Clementi (1752–1832) was Italian by birth but settled in England as a young man, becoming famous as a pianist, teacher and composer. All slurs and dynamics are Clementi's own, except for the hairpins in bars 14–16, which are editorial suggestions only.
Source: *Eleventh Edition with great improvements of Clementi's Introduction to the art of playing on the Piano Forte*, Op. 42 (London, 1826).

C:1

Friday

from *Seven Days a Week*

RICHARD RODNEY BENNETT

Arioso in F

No. 1 from *Zwölf Handstücke*

B:3

TÜRK

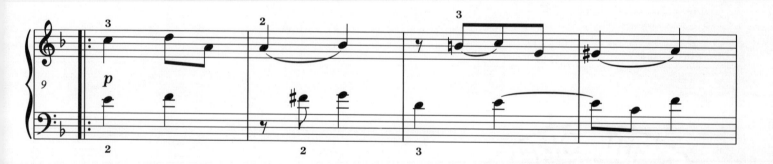

This Arioso is the first of 'Twelve Pieces for Use in Instruction' by the Halle organist Daniel Gottlob Türk (1750–1813). He included them as an appendix in his monumental *Klavierschule,* the most influential keyboard instruction manual of its day. Türk tells us that the finger should be raised from the key on the last note of a phrase, i.e. on the second treble note of bars 4, 8 & 12. These bars should thus be phrased.

Source: *Zwölf Handstücke zum Gebrauche beym Unterrichten, Klavierschule* (Leipzig & Halle, 1789)

Calypso Joe

No. 9 from *Finger Jogging Boogie*

STEPHEN DURO

C:2

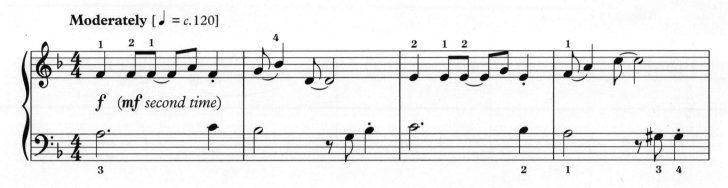

C:3

The Swinging Sioux

WILLIAM GILLOCK

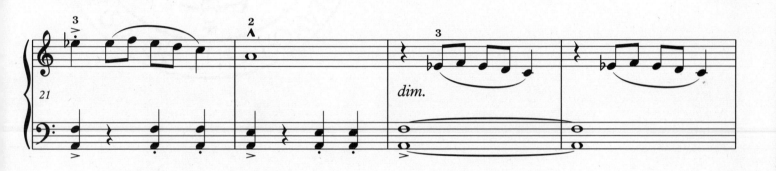